Hola, I'm Dora!
This is my friend Boots.
We are going on a new adventure.
Will you come with us?
Great, let's go! ¡Vámanos!

£6.99

Contents

NICK JR. DORA the EXPLORER

Official Annual

Published by ALLIGATOR BOOKS LIMITED
Gadd House, Arcadia Avenue, London N3 2JU.
Printed in China.

ALLIGATOR

Meet Dora and Friends

Get to know all your friends. Who likes to play soccer? Who loves bananas

DORA
THE EXPLORER

Dora lives in a big yellow house with her Mami and Papi.

Languages: Spanish and English

Favourite activities: Exploring, taking pictures with her camera and visiting her abuela

Favourite game: Soccer

Favourite instrument: Flute

Favourite food: Blueberries

BOOTS
THE MONKEY

Boots lives in a treehouse with his Mummy and Daddy.

Favourite activities: Swinging on vines, learning Spanish and riding with Rojo the Firetruck

Language: English

Favourite instrument: Maraccas

Favourite food: Bananas

Favourite colour: Red! Like his boots, cowboy hat and pyjamas.

TICO
THE SQUIRREL

Tico lives in a tree in the Nutty Forest.

Language: Spanish

Favourite activities: Driving his yellow car and flying his bicycle-plane

Favourite instrument: Harmonica

Favourite food: Nuts, nuts and more nuts!

ISA
THE IGUANA

Isa lives in the Flowery Garden.

Favourite activity: Riding on her rocket ship

Language: English

Favourite instrument: Trombone

Favourite food: Cupcakes

BENNY
THE BULL

Benny lives in a red barn with his grandma.

Favourite activity: Riding in his hot air balloon

Language: English

Favourite game: Baseball

Favourite instrument: Conga drum

SWIPER
THE FOX

Swiper the Fox lives on Blueberry Hill.

Favourite activities: Swiping and hiding, flying in his foxchopper and riding his motor scooter

Language: English

Favourite food: Cowboy cookies

Did you know?: Swiper is a master of disguise, he's pretended to be a pirate, a snowman and even an egg!

MAMI

Mami and hugs go together.

She lives in a yellow house with Papi and Dora.

Language: Spanish and English

Favourite song: 'Sana, Sana'. Mami sings it to Dora.

Did you know?: Mami is an archaeologist. She digs for treasures.

PAPI

Papi and baseball go together! He's the coach of Dora's baseball team.

Language: Spanish and English

Favourite activity: Mambo dancing

Did you know?: Papi loves to cook!

ABUELA

Abuela and storytelling go together. She lives in una casa rosada, a pink house.

Language: Spanish and English

Favourite song: '¡Bate, Bate'. 'Chocolate!'

Favourite food: Azrez con leche

Dynamic Duos

Draw a line between each pair to make a match.
Use these word clues to help you find each pair.

dog / bone
el perro / el hueso

key / lock
la llave / la cerradura

drum / drumsticks
el tambor / los palillos

ball / bat
la pelota / el bate

Dot to Dot Fun

Join the dots from 1-30
to see what Dora is looking at!

12

Time for Colouring

Mixed-Up Jungle

Something's silly en la selva. There are six silly things, in fact.
Look for animals that aren't quite right and count them:
Uno, dos, tres, cuatro, cinco, seis.

This isn't the jungle, it's a curtain hiding the City of Lost Toys. We need the curtain to go UP and take us to page 56. Say "¡Arriba!"

Fly Away Day

What could Dora do on a windy day?

The was bright. Dora wanted to play!

The outside was blowing in the breeze.

The wind called to , "Come and play, please.

We can sail the Tico gave to Boots.

Or make float down like parachutes!"

 had an idea he wanted to try.

"Let's make a . It can fly!"

Now try it with some Spanish words.

the sun — el sol
the tree — el árbol
the kite — la cometa
bubbles — las burbujas
a paper aeroplane — un avión de papel

Up, Up and Away

Oh, no! Our extra special aeroplane flew away in a breeze.
Which way did it go? Follow the trails with your finger.

Benny Helps Out

Dora and Boots search for the aeroplane in Benny's balloon, but they can't find it. Where is the aeroplane? Look for pairs of trees and draw a line between them. Then find the aeroplane in the tree that is left.

La Fiesta

Let's have a paper aeroplane party. Isa has her *VERDE* aeroplane, Tico has his *ROJO* aeroplane and Benny has his *AZUL* aeroplane. The Fiesta Trio need their planes too, but Swiper has hidden them. They are coloured *AMARILLO*, *MORADO*, and *ROSADO*. Can you find them?

Time for Colouring

Ice Cream Hunt

¡Hola, I'm Dora! This is my friend Boots.
We love ice cream. Do you love ice cream?

We just missed the ice cream truck, and
we're going to find it. Will you help us?

Great, let's go! ¡Vámanos!

There's Benny! Do you see what he's eating?

Yes, an ice cream cone!

Benny says the ice cream truck is going to Coney Island. We have to go to Coney Island, Boots!

But how will we get there? I'll check with Map.

Map says we have to go over Strawberry Mountain, then row a boat across Chocolate Lake, then walk over a bridge to get to Coney Island.

Over Strawberry Mountain, across Chocolate Lake, over a bridge to Coney Island. Let's go! ¡Vámanos!

Do you remember where we have to go first? Do you remember, Boots?

That's right. Strawberry Mountain.

Do you see Strawberry Mountain?

It sure is big. How will we get over the mountain?

Look, there is Tico up ahead in his little car. Let's call out to him. I'm sure he will drive us over the mountain.

Tico! Tico!

Tico is driving Boots and I over Strawberry Mountain. Graçias, Tico. Thanks.

Where do we have to go next?

Do you remember?

That's right. Chocolate Lake!

Do you see Chocolate Lake?

Oh, yeah, there it is. Thanks for helping!

First we went over Strawberry Mountain. Now we have to row a boat across Chocolate Lake. Then we can get to Coney Island to find the ice cream truck.

I think we're nearly there, Boots. There's chocolate everywhere. Wow, there's a tree with chocolate, whipped cream and a cherry on top! Do you see the cherry?

We made it! We found Chocolate Lake! Now we need a boat to cross the lake.

Oh, no! I think Swiper was here. There's no boat!
Do you see Swiper?

Let's look in the forest for the boat.

Do you see the boat?

I see it too. Thanks for helping. Graçias.

Now we can row across Chocolate Lake.

Hey, look, Coney Island!

We went over Strawberry Mountain in Tico's car, we rowed the boat across Chocolate Lake. Now we can cross the bridge to get to Coney Island.

Then we can find the ice cream truck and get some ice cream!

We did it, ¡Excelente!
We're on Coney Island!

I think the ice cream truck is behind one of the big cones. Let's go get our ice cream Boots!

Thank you for helping us get to Coney Island! See you later!

Time for Colouring

It looks like Boots got his ice cream after all!

Big River Boot Hunt

¡Hola, I'm Dora.

This is my best friend, Boots.

We have a problem.

Boots was swinging on this tree branch and one of his boots fell off - into the river!

Will you help us find it?

Let's check with Map.
Map knows where the
river goes.

First the river goes under the bridge... and then it goes past the
Froggy Rocks... and then it gets to the waterfall.

¡Vámanos! Let's go to the bridge, it's just down the river.

There's your boot, Boots. Do you see it floating down the river?

We need something to ride on the river. Then we can catch the boot.

Here's a boat! But it's missing some pieces. I think the pieces are behind the tree. How many pieces do we need? Can you count them with me? One, two, three, four, five, six, seven!

¡Muy bien! Good counting!

Wait, I think I hear Swiper! He might want to swipe our boat! Swiper, no swiping!

The boat is ready, and there are life jackets inside. Time to head for the bridge!

We made it to the bridge.

But look, Boots, your boot is on the other side of it. Our boat won't fit under the bridge.

I know, Tico will open it for us, there he is!

Remember, Tico speaks Spanish, so we have to say '¡Abre!' Open!

That was nice of Tico to help open the bridge for us.

Next we go to... The Rocks! Right! The Froggy Rocks!

Now where are the rocks? Do you see the rocks?
Come on, vámanos. I see your boot, Boots!

Watch out for all the frogs. How many can you count?

Those rocks sure look big! We have to row around the rocks or we'll crash right into them!

Row, row, row!

Phew! We made it past Froggy Rocks! But where is your boot, Boots?

Oh, no! The boot is going over the waterfall!

We can't go over the waterfall. We need a way around it.

Do you see a way around the waterfall?

Graçias.

Thanks for helping us to find this little river that goes around the waterfall.

But we still haven't found the boot!

First, let's look for everything red.
A butterfly... a fish... a flower
There it is.... Do you see the boot?

48

Let's paddle over and get it, Boots.

¡Fantastico! Well done!

We've got your boot!

Yay! We did it with your help!

We went under the bridge...

and past the rocks...

We went around
the waterfall.

We said 'abre' at the
bridge... so we could get
through... Boots lost his boot...

But we found it... whoo-hoo!

¡Adios! See you later!

All Together

Yay! We did it with help from our friends.
Draw a picture of tus mejores amigos, your very best friends!

¡Sí, lo hicimos... juntos!

We did it...together!

Where Do We Go?

Who do we ask for help when we don't know which way to go?
Connect the dots in this order to finish the picture.

Start here
with ROJO.

If there's
a place
you've got
to go,
I'm the one
you need
to know!

Say "Map!"
Say "Map!"

Mi Mapa

On a map, simple pictures show places. Draw pictures in the boxes to make a map of your own.

Pick a place you want to go. Then draw two places that you pass along the way.

library

house

park

city

beach

If there's a place you've got to go, I'm the one you need to know!

Where's Boots?

Let's explore with Boots. But where can that monkey be? Do you see him? Boots has red boots, so let's look for something RED.

Can you spot these other things coloured *ROJO*?

bird
el pájaro

flower
la flor

balloon
el globo

oar
el remo

butterfly
la mariposa

Watch out for Swiper! Do you see him?

Lost and Found

We're looking for things in the City of Lost Toys. Will you help us?

for Dora   for Swiper   for Tico   for Azul   for Isa   for Benny

Walk This Way

Let's follow these footprints to see who made them!

How To Play This Game

To start, you'll need two or more players, a dice, and playing pieces, such as coins. When it's your turn, roll the dice to see how many spaces to move. Then use your fingers to walk along the footprints. Mark your place with a coin. If you land on a space with a picture, do the action you see in the matching picture below. Then take an extra turn. Play until everyone reaches Boots!

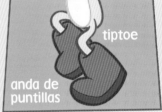

tiptoe
anda de puntillas

run
corre

jump
salta

ABC Fiesta

A Arroz
RICE

B Bananas
BANANAS

C Cerezas
CHERRIES

D Dulce
CANDY

E Enchiladas

F Flan

G Guacamole

¡Hola, soy Dora! And you're invited to our fiesta. Look at the yummy foods, one for each letter of the alphabet. A is for arroz, B is for bananas, and C is for cerezas! Can you find all the foods in the picture below? Hmmm…delicioso!

H Huevos
EGGS

I Icaco
COCOA PLUM

J Jugo
JUICE

K Kiwi

L Leche
MILK

M Manzana
APPLE

60

Z Zanahorias CARROTS

Y Yautia CHAYOTE YAMS

X eXtra helpings!

W Waffles

V Vegetales VEGETABLES

U Uvas GRAPES

T Tortillas

S Salsa

O Orozuz LICORICE

P Pollo CHICKEN

Q Queso CHEESE

R Ravioles RAVIOLI

Glossary

Words for Objects, People, Places, Ideas:

open - **abre** - say 'AH-bray'

up - **arriba** - say 'a-REE-ba'

tree - **el árbol** - say 'el AR-bole'

a paper aeroplane - **un avión de papel**
- say 'oon avee-ON day pa-PEL'

bat - **el bate** - say 'el BA-tay'

bubbles - **las burbujas** - say 'lahs bur-BEWH-as'

a house - **una casa** - say 'OO-na CA-sa'

lock - **la cerradura** - say 'la serra-DOO-ra'

kite - **la cometa** - say 'la KO-MET-ah'

run - **corre** - say 'cor-EH'

in - **en** - say 'en'

flower - **la flor** - say 'la flor'

balloon - **el globo** - say 'el GLOH-bo'

bone - **el hueso** - say 'el HWAY-so'

key - **la llave** - say 'la YA-vay'

butterfly - **la mariposa** - say 'la mah-ray-POH-sa'

bird - **el pájaro** - say 'el PA-ha-roh'

drumsticks - **los palillos** - say 'lohs pa-LEE-yohs'

ball - **la pelota** - say 'la pel-OH-ta'

dog - **el perro** - say 'el PAYR-oh'

oar - **el remo** - say 'el RAY-moh'

jump - **salta** - say 'sal-TA'

jungle - **la selva** - say 'la SEL-va'

the sun - **el sol** - say 'el sohl'

drum - **el tambor** - say 'el tam-BOR'